D1591013

Vietnam War FACTS QUIZ

Vietnam

War

FACTS QUIZ

by Erhard Konerding

THE TRUTH
& DRAMA
OF AMERICAN
INVOLVEMENT

PRESENTED IN
A MULTIPLE CHOICE
FORMAT

THE SOUTHFARM PRESS
Middletown, CT

THE SOUTHFARM PRESS
A division of
Haan Graphic Publishing Services, Ltd.
P.O. Box 1296
Middletown, CT 06457

Copyright © 1986 by The Southfarm Press
Cover design Copyright © 1986 by
Haan Graphic Publishing Services, Ltd.

ISBN: 0-913337-07-2
Library of Congress Catalogue Card Number: 85-063489

All rights reserved, which includes the right to reproduce
this book or portions thereof in any form whatsoever.
For information address The Southfarm Press,
P.O. Box 1296, Middletown, CT 06457.

First Printing: February, 1986

Printed in the United States of America

Composition by Typegraphics,
Marlborough, Connecticut

ACKNOWLEDGEMENTS
Photographs courtesy of Martin Reisch, Bell Helicopter
Textron; Chip Hewlett, Browning; Tom Williams,
Camillus Cutlery, Inc.; Lucretia Clifton, Gerber
Legendary Blades; Bruce Goulding, Kaman Aerospace
Corporation; David Holt, Patton Museum of Cavalry
and Armor; Gary T. Randall, Randall Made Knives;
Robert Grueskin, Springfield Armory, Inc.; Maj. William
Austin, Air Force Office of Public Affairs; R.L. Scheina,
Historian, U.S. Coast Guard; Robert Carlisle, U.S. Navy
Office of Information; Mrs. Arlene Washenik; Sikorsky Aircraft

CONTENTS

Answers are located at the end of each chapter.

In Memory Of My High School Classmate And Friend

GARY WASHENIK

National Merit Finalist, "Most Intellectual",
Westinghouse Science Talent Search Award

SP5 U.S. Army; Medical Aidman, 101st Airborne

Killed August 16, 1970, Firebase Ripcord,
Quang Tri Province, Vietnam

"He believed in saving lives, not destroying them."

Chapter 1:

C-RATS AND BOONIE HATS:
LIFE IN-COUNTRY

Service in Vietnam, a place "In-Country", was a unique experience, full of strange sights and sounds. GI's had to quickly get used to heat, humidity, a new language, and war without front lines, where anyone was a potential enemy.

1. Most U.S. servicemen arrived in Vietnam:

A. On a U.S. Air Force transport plane
B. On a chartered commercial airliner
C. On a U.S. Army transport ship
D. On a U.S. Navy transport ship

2. ___ True or False: U.S. servicemen served a standard tour of approximately 12 months.

3. ___ True or False: Army troops arrived in Vietnam in units of platoon size or larger, which were joined with the unit they had served and trained with in the U.S.

4. ___ True or False: Many GI's counted down the days until rotation home with a "short-timer's calendar", often marked on the helmet cover or notched on a "short-timer's stick".

5. The "Freedom Bird" was:

A. A Medevac or rescue helicopter
B. A C-119 gunship
C. A forward control light aircraft
D. A plane taking troops home to the United States

6. The olive drab towel issued to Army troops in Vietnam was often:

A. Worn as a neck scarf or headband to absorb sweat
B. Worn under the rucksack to keep the straps from cutting into the shoulders
C. Worn as a loincloth in place of the uniform trousers
D. A and B above

7. "Steam and cream" was the popular name for:

A. The standard treatment received by patrons of Vietnamese "massage parlors."
B. White phosphorus shells
C. A bowl or steamed rice topped with fish sauce, a favorite Vietnamese dish
D. Chipped beef on toast

The U.S. Army Special Forces were commonly known as the "Green Berets" for their special headgear. Other forces soon adopted berets. Match up the proper color with its users:

8. ___ Red
9. ___ Maroon
10. ___ Black
11. ___ Dark Blue
12. ___ Air Force Blue

A. Korean Special Forces, Australian armored forces, Viet "Black Panther" men, some LRRP's, USN Junk Forces, and Riverines
B. Air Force pararescuemen (PJ's), Vietnam rangers
C. Vietnamese paratroopers
D. Air Force combat controllers
E. Air Force Security Police

13. The armored "flak jacket" was worn by:

A. Air Force, Navy, and Marine Corps jet pilots only
B. Combat infantrymen
C. Ground troops in general
D. B and C above

14. The standard olive drab fatigue uniform and leather combat boots worn by American soldiers and airmen in temperate zones:

A. Was the standard American combat uniform in Vietnam until the end of the war, despite complaints about discomfort in the heat and humidity. The lighter replacement uniform was not ready until 1975
B. Was replaced by "jungle fatigues", made of lightweight ripstop cotton
C. Was replaced by cotton-nylon "Battle-dress utilities" (BDU) in a camouflage pattern

15. The leather combat boot:

A. Was kept throughout the war, despite the fact that it rotted and fell apart in the jungle
B. Was replaced by the "jungle boot" of leather, nylon and canvas, with a "Panama tread" sole and ventilation holes
C. Was replaced by a high-top basketball type sneaker, dyed olive green
D. Was replaced by the "gladiator sandal", a laced, open sandal which prevented foot disease

16. The "boonie hat" was:

A. An olive green cotton baseball cap with a stiff visor and front
B. A soft, floppy hat with all-around brim and vent holes, in either olive or camouflage
C. Similar to the drill instructor's "Smokey" hat, but in cotton and nylon

17. Air Force personnel wore the same basic uniform as Army troops, with different insignia. Which of the following statements are true?

A. Airmen were not allowed to roll up uniform sleeves without an order from the flight surgeon in charge of the area
B. Air Force combat controllers dressed in the same unique fashion as Army Long Range Patrols
C. Air Force men began wearing the same jungle fatigue uniform as Army men
D. All of the above

18. The Army switched to "subdued" rank and unit insignia. These were:
A. Black on green (dark blue on green for Air Force)
B. Intended to make officers and men less visible and conspicuous
C. Worn inside uniforms and headgear
D. All of the above
E. A and B only
F. B and C only

19. The standard G.I. "steel pot" helmet:
A. Was generally worn with a cloth camouflage cover held in place with an elastic band, often used as a storage place for cigarettes, insect repellent, lucky charms, photographs, etc.
B. Was often adorned with graffiti, including countdown calendars of days remaining in Vietnam before going home
C. Was frequently replaced by various hats or headscarves
D. All of the above

Some typical vocabulary:

20. ___ G.I.	A.	To slog around on foot
21. ___ Hump	B.	One's commander
22. ___ P-38	C.	Native name for American troops
(John Wayne)	D.	Small folding can opener
23. ___ Six		

More vocabulary matching:

24. ___ Klick	A.	General term for Army soldiers, used by
25. ___ Point		people like MP's
26. ___ Slack	B.	First man in a patrol
27. ___ Troop	C.	Second man in a patrol
	D.	A kilometer (.62 miles)

Match these:

28. ___ Wake-up	A.	Newly-arrived soldier
29. ___ Cherry,	B.	Soldier whose tour is nearly over
or NFG	C.	One's last day in Vietnam, when the "Freedom
30. ___ Short-timer		Bird" takes him home to "The World"

31. This American serviceman wearing his "boonie hat" is armed with:

A. A Remington 1100 12 gauge shotgun
B. A LAW (66 mm. light antitank weapon)
C. An M-79 40 mm. grenade launcher
D. A Soviet RPG-2 antitank rocket

32. Soldiers, marines, sailors, and airmen serving in Vietnam were paid in:

A. Military payment certificates, commonly called "scrip"
B. U.S. silver certificates
C. Certified checks
D. U.S. Savings Bonds

33. Conscientious objectors who were classed 1-A-0, and objected only to killing and not to military service, were trained as noncombatants. They served in Vietnam as:

A. Medical aidmen (most medics were C.O.'s)
B. Clerks and cooks
C. Drivers
D. All of the above
E. B and C only

Answer Key

1. B	2. True	3. False	4. True
5. D	6. D	7. A	8. C
9. B	10. A	11. D	12. E
13. D	14. B	15. B	16. B
17. D	18. E	19. D	20. C
21. A	22. D	23. B	24. D
25. B	26. C	27. A	28. C
29. A	30. B	31. C	32. A
33. D			

Chapter 2:
GEOGRAPHY

Vietnam was a strange, exotic place for both servicemen serving there and Americans at home. The odd place names and unfamiliar ways caused culture shock among many GI's and U.S. officials stationed there.

South Vietnam was split up from North to South into 4 Corps Tactical Zones, each assigned a Roman numeral. Where was each located?

1. ___ I Corps (often pronounced   A. Area around Saigon
       "Eye" Corps)   B. A narrow strip in the North,
2. ___ II Corps   bordering North Vietnam
3. ___ III Corps   C. The Central Highlands and
4. ___ IV Corps   adjoining plains area
                                    D. The Mekong Delta, full of
                                       mangrove swamps, rice paddies,
                                       and people

5. The main street of Saigon (Freedom Street), known for its shops, bars, and massage parlors, was called in Vietnamese:

A. Non La street
B. Hoa Hao street
C. Tu Do street
D. Ding Hao street

6. ___ True or False: In Vietnamese, "Mekong" means "9 Dragons" and the Mekong Delta was called the "Mouth of the Dragon".

7. The Southeast Asia Treaty Organization was pledged to defend South Vietnam against aggression. Five of the SEATO nations sent combat troops to Vietnam. Which did not?

A. United States   E. Australia
B. United Kingdom   F. Philippines
C. France   G. Thailand
D. New Zealand   H. Pakistan

8. War Zones C and D were two areas infested with Vietcong. They were:

A. Near Saigon
B. Deep in the Mekong Delta
C. In the Central Highlands
D. Near the border with North Vietnam and Laos

9. ___ True or False: The Fish Hook, Angel's Wing, and Parrot's Beak were all areas in southern South Vietnam, on the Cambodian border.

Match these bases or battlefields with their general area:

10. ___ Michelin Plantation,   A. Northern South Vietnam, near
        Ho Bo Woods and   North Vietnam
        Iron Triangle   B. Near Saigon
11. ___ Pleiku, Ben Het,   C. Central Highlands
        Ban Me Thuot
12. ___ Khe Sanh, Camp Carroll,
        Rock Pile

13. At the Potsdam Conference at the end of World War II, the Allies divided Vietnam on an arbitrary line, south of which the 20th Indian Division, under British General Douglas Gracey would supervise the Japanese surrender, north of which the Nationalist Chinese would do the same. The dividing line was the:

A. 16th Parallel
B. 17th Parallel
C. 18th Parallel

14. The Ho Chi Minh Trail, main infiltration route from North Vietnam to South Vietnam, was:

A. A six-lane paved highway, lighted at night
B. Footpaths unsuitable for any kind of vehicles
C. A web of tracks used for foot, bicycle, and truck traffic
D. A tunnel dug through solid rock, in one of North Vietnam's greatest engineering achievements

15. In 1966, the Ho Chi Minh Trail was about 820 miles long. By 1972, it was:

A. Only half as long
B. Nearly twice as long
C. Over three times as long
D. Nearly 10 times as long

16. South Vietnam was not all jungle. Parts of it were mountain, plain, swamp, or sprawling city. Still, jungle and tropical forest with trees reaching 200 to 250 feet in height covered:

A. 25% of South Vietnam
B. 40% of South Vietnam
C. 60% of South Vietnam
D. 85% of South Vietnam

17. "Karst" describes a type of region seen in Indochina. It is:

A. Reedy, marshy swampland, as seen in the Mekong Delta
B. Dry plains, typical of plateaus in the Central Highlands
C. Steep limestone ridges, as often shown in Chinese paintings

FACT:

American authorities selected 10 locations where American troops could take "R and R", a one-week vacation from the war. They were:

Hong Kong	Honolulu, Hawaii
Kuala Lumpur, Malaysia	Singapore
Tokyo	Bangkok, Thailand
Sydney, Australia	Naha, Okinawa
Taipei, Taiwan	Manila, Philippines

18. "LBJ" was the name for:

A. Long Binh Jail, the Army stockade
B. Laotian Broad Jungle
C. Liet Bich Junction, where Highways 6 and 11 crossed
D. Lying Broad Jump, the contortion necessary when one's sleeping quarters were shelled

19. In January, 1963 the Vietcong defeated a larger force of ARVN's (South Vietnamese Army) equipped with helicopters, armored personnel carriers, and American advisors at the battle of:

A. Ap Bac
B. Sui Tre
C. Dau Tieng
D. Rha De

20. The last major battle of 1967, fought at Dak To near the Ben Het Special Forces camp with the heaviest fighting in that area to date, was in the area of:

A. The Mekong Delta
B. The suburbs of Saigon
C. The Central Highlands
D. The Demilitarized Zone (DMZ)

Several major American operations took place in 1966 and 1967. When and where?

21. ___ Junction City   A. Iron Triangle, January 1967
22. ___ Cedar Falls   B. War Zone C, February 1967
23. ___ Attleboro   C. Binh Dinh Province, late 1966

24. These operations were named for:

A. Army Bases in the American southwest
B. American towns
C. Counties in Texas

25. In October and November 1965, the North Vietnamese and Vietcong forces attempted to cut South Vietnam in two. Where did they strike?

A. In the Ia Drang valley
B. Near the town of Pleiku
C. The Central Highlands area
D. All of the above

Place the following geographical features with their approximate location:

26. Monkey Mountain
27. Nui Ba Den (Black Virgin Mountain)
28. Mu Gia Pass
29. The "Citadel"

A. Dau Tieng (N.W. of Saigon)
B. Laos
C. Da Nang
D. Hue

Answer Key

1. B	2. C	3. A	4. D
5. C	6. True	7. B, C, H	8. A
9. True	10. B	11. C	12. A
13. A	14. C	15. C	16. C
17. C	18. A	19. A	20. C
21. B	22. A	23. C	24. B
25. D	26. C	27. A	28. B
29. D			

Chapter 3:
PEOPLE

1. General George Patton, son of the famous World War II American commander:

A. Commanded the 11th Armored Cavalry in South Vietnam
B. Served in the Military Police in Vietnam, and helped fend off the Vietcong attack on the American Embassy in Saigon during the Tet Offensive
C. Was a Quartermaster Corps officer in Germany during the Vietnam war, and never saw combat
D. Was a conscientious objector to all wars, and served in a civilian hospital in San Francisco during the war

FACT:

U.S. Navy SEAL team aboard a riverine craft. The SEAL acronym stands for Sea, Air, and Land.

2. Bob Hope went to Vietnam to entertain the troops every year from 1964 to 1972. His shows were always at (on):

A. The Fourth of July
B. Thanksgiving
C. Christmas

3. Can you put the Secretaries of Defense during the Vietnam conflict in proper chronological order?

A. Clark Clifford
B. Melvin Laird
C. Robert McNamara

4. Which of these men was *not* an American ambassador to South Vietnam?

A. Gen. Maxwell Taylor
B. Henry Cabot Lodge
C. Cyrus Vance
D. Ellsworth Bunker

5. The U.S. government was indirectly involved in the overthrow of South Vietnamese President Ngo Dinh Diem. General Duong Van Minh was Diem's successor. Who succeeded him?

A. General Khanh
B. Nguyen Van Thieu
C. Nguyen Cao Ky

6. In July, 1972, two Americans toured North Vietnam in a controversial visit. They were (2 correct answers):

A. Jane Fonda
B. Ann-Margret
C. Ramsey Clark
D. Edward M. Kennedy

7. What did Sylvester Stallone, who speaks up for Vietnam veterans in his "Rambo" movies, do during the Vietnam War?

A. Served in the Green Berets as a staff sergeant, advising the Montagnard tribes in the Central Highlands
B. Was an Air Force enlisted man and aircraft armorer in Thailand
C. Endured the siege of Khe Sanh as a Marine lance corporal, and was wounded there twice
D. Went to college in Switzerland, and avoided service altogether

FACT:

A Number of Senators and Congressmen served in Vietnam, some with great distinction. Among them:

Senator Jeremiah Denton: Republican of Alabama; Navy pilot; spent over 7 years as a POW in North Vietnam; awarded Medal of Honor
Senator John Kerry: Democrat of Massachusetts; Awarded Silver Star, Bronze Star, Purple Heart; National coordinator, Vietnam Veterans Against the War, 1969-71
Senators Larry Pressler, Republican of South Dakota, and **Albert Gore, Jr.,** Republican of Tennessee: served in the U.S. Army in Vietnam

In the House of Representatives:

John S. McCain, Arizona: U.S. Navy, POW 1967-73
Jim Kolbe, Arizona: Lt., U.S. Navy in Vietnam
Duncan Hunter, California: 1st Lt., U.S. Army Airborne
Hank Brown, Colorado: Lt., U.S. Navy Forward Air Controller
Thomas Carper, Delaware: U.S. Navy
Robert Smith, New Hampshire: U.S. Navy
Denny Smith, Oregon: 180 combat missions over Vietnam, 1965-66
John P. Murtha, Pennsylvania: Maj., USMC at Da Nang
Thomas Daschle, South Dakota: 1st Lt., USAF
Ben Garrido Blaz, Delegate from Guam: USMC officer
Robert K. Dornan, California: served before Vietnam; during the war, he originated the POW bracelet
David Bonior, Michigan: author, *The Vietnam Veteran: A History of Neglect*
Bill Hendon, North Carolina: member Congressional Task Force on POW's and MIA's in Southeast Asia

8. Many stars of stage and screen entertained the troops in Vietnam. Which one of them missed the show one night in 1967 and put her nurse's training to use, treating wounded men in a Mekong Delta area hospital?

A. Phyllis Diller
B. Joey Heatherton
C. Martha Raye
D. Nancy Sinatra

Over 200 soldiers, sailors, airmen and marines won the Medal of Honor, America's highest military decoration, for service in Vietnam. Can you answer the following questions about the Medal?

9. ___True or False: More Medals of Honor were awarded for service in Vietnam than for actions in the Korean War.

10. Many soldiers, marines, and sailors received the Medal of Honor for protecting their buddies by falling on or blocking exploding grenades, mines, or booby traps. Some of these men survived the explosion or found the grenade a dud. How many medals were won, posthumously or not?

A. 3
B. 14
C. 25
D. 71

11. A conscientious objector was awarded the Medal of Honor for bravery while a medical aidman in Vietnam. The last Medal of Honor given was awarded to:

A. A returning prisoner of war
B. The man on whom Sylvester Stallone based "Rambo"
C. The Vietnam Unknown, interred at Arlington National Cemetery with the Unknowns from pervious wars

---

FACT:

The only Army nurse killed by enemy action in Vietnam was 1st Lt. Sharon A. Lane, ANC, who died June 8, 1969 in a rocket attack on the 312th Evacuation Hospital at Chu Lai.

12. In addition to the many showbiz stars who toured Vietnam, a number of sports heroes also visited the men there, including a tour of baseball players in 1967. Who was not among them?

A. Joe DiMaggio
B. Pete Rose
C. Tony Conigliaro
D. Roberto Clemente

13. ___True or False:Reservists and National Guard members were never called to active duty for the war in Vietnam.

14. ___ True or False: The U.S. Marine Corps, as in World War II, was not an all-volunteer force and accepted draftees.

Many young soldiers in Vietnam enjoyed the same music as the young people at home, many of whom were protesting against the war.

15. ___ True or False: In 1966, *The Ballad of the Green Berets* by SSgt. Barry Sadler, hit the top of the charts for weeks and sold over a million records.

Can you match these singing groups with their lead singers?

16. ___ Jim Morrison   A. Creedence Clearwater Revival
17. ___ John Fogerty   B. The Doors
18. ___ Smokey Robinson   C. The Rolling Stones
19. ___ Mick Jagger   D. The Temptations

FACT:

Ho Chi Minh, an enigmatic figure with a wispy beard, was leader of North Vietnam. He had previously been a steward aboard a French ship, a petitioner at the Versailles Conference after World War I, and a founding member of the French Communist Party. A Soviet agent in China in the 1930's, Ho (then called Nguyen Ai Quoc) was imprisoned by Chiang Kai-shek's Kuomintang in the 1940's, entered Hanoi as a victor in August, 1945, and was later pursued by the French. His Vietminh emerged victorious in 1954.

20. Capt. Steve Ritchie and Capt. Chuck DeBellevue, two of the five American aces of the Vietnam War, are shown here. They were officers in the:

A. U.S. Air Force
B. U.S. Navy
C. U.S. Marine Corps

Answer Key

1. A	2. C	3. C, A, B	4. C
5. A	6. A and C	7. D	8. A
9. True	10. D	11. C	12. D
13. False	14. True	15. True	16. B
17. A	18. D	19. C	20. A

Chapter 4

VIET-SPEAK

GI's in Vietnam spoke a strange language combining English, military terms and slang, and Vietnamese and other Asian languages, often termed "Viet-Speak." The Army Reporter, official Army newspaper in Vietnam, printed a classic fairy tale in this strange tongue, in 1971.

Little Red Riding Hood is leaving her hootch with a basket of chop-chop to take to her sick grandma-san. . . .As she places the basket next to the bed, she makes a double-take and exclaims, "Choi-oi! What big eyeballs you have!"

"There it is," says the wolf. "All the better to see you with."

"And your ears are maxed to the onions," comments the hood.

"Check it out. All the better to hear you with."

Distinctly Vietnamese words along with words borrowed from the French comprised a major part of the lingo used in Vietnam. Match Vietnamese words (or phonetic rendering) with English equivalent:

1. ___ ba-me-ba
2. ___ bic (biet)
3. ___ bookoo (beaucoup)
4. ___ caca dow
5. ___ choi oi
6. ___ dinky-dow

A. understand
B. "I'll kill you" (facetiously)
C. You're crazy
D. Many, or lots of
E. 33 (Vietnamese beer)
F. Good heavens

7. GI's called the Vietcong "Charley" or similar names because:

A. It was the closest they could get to pronouncing "Chiua Li," the Vietcong's name for itself
B. It was short for "Victor Charlie," the phonetic alphabet symbol for "V.C."
C. The Vietcong were first encountered at the Battle of the Shar A Lie River
D. The first V.C. captured was named Charles

Many Vietnamese words sounded quite similar to the American ear, but meant very different things. Three rhyming examples:

8. ___ Ao Dai   A. One-time Emperor of Vietnam, installed by
9. ___ Bao Dai   the French
10. ___ Cao Dai   B. Religious and political group in South
                               Vietnam
                   C. Traditional slit skirt and trousers ensemble
                           worn by Vietnamese women

Deck crewmen aboard U.S. Navy aircraft carriers stationed in the Gulf of Tonkin wore jerseys of distinctive colors to identify their function. Match shirt color with function:

11. ___ Blue shirt   A. Firefighting and crash rescue
12. ___ Green shirt   B. Refueling
13. ___ Purple shirt   C. Aircraft handlers
14. ___ Red shirt   D. Aircraft spotters
15. ___ Yellow shirt   E. Catapult, arresting gear, and
                               maintenance

16. Two multi-purpose phrases often heard in Vietnam were "Sorry about that!" and "Would you believe?" These expressions were first popularized by:

A. "Murray the K", New York disc jockey
B. Don Adams, in the *Get Smart* TV series
C. Roger Moore, in the James Bond movie *You Only Live Twice*
D. Bob Hope, in his annual Christmas tour of Vietnam

Vietnamese Vocabulary, Part 1:

17. ___ Non La   A. You are lying!
18. ___ Nuoc Nam   B. Sorry!
19. ___ Sao (rhymes with how)   C. A little bit
20. ___ Sin loy   D. Conical hat, part of traditional
21. ___ Tee-tee   Vietnamese costume
                         E. Fermented fish sauce, called
                         "armpit sauce" by many

Acronyms abounded in Vietnam, as in all military environments. What do these mean?

22. ___ CYA   A. Name for U.S. command in Vietnam
23. ___ DEROS   B. "Let's not get things too complicated"
24. ___ KISS   C. "Don't let yourself get caught unprepared"
25. ___ MACV   D. End of tour, when you get to go home

Servicemen had names for each other, too. Who was called what?

26. ___ Redleg, or cannon cocker   A. Infantryman
27. ___ REMF   B. Airman
28. ___ Grunt, or boonie rat   C. Top sergeant
29. ___ Zoomie   D. Artilleryman
30. ___ First shirt   E. Support or non-combat troops

Vietnamese Vocabulary, Part 2:

31. ___ Co   A. Vietcong special forces
32. ___ Dac Cong   B. Come home, or go home
33. ___ Di Di   C. Amnesty program for surrendered Vietcong
34. ___ Chieu Hoi D. Vietcong who surrendered under amnesty
35. ___ Hoi Chanh   program
                   E. Unmarried woman, "Miss"

Air Force personnel, many of whom were stationed in Thailand, had their own unique slang, including:

36. ___ Lazy Dog   A. Aiming dot on aircraft Head-Up-Display
37. ___ Dragon Ship   B. Rear seat crew member in F-4 aircraft
38. ___ GIB   C. To manuever wildly to avoid enemy anti-
39. ___ Pipper   aircraft fire and missiles
40. ___ Jink   D. A type of aerial bomb
                      E. AC-47 transport converted into heavily armed
                          ground attack aircraft

Sometimes, a word or phrase was used in different senses by Army versus Air Force men:

41. ___ True or False: In Army parlance, "frag" refers to the practice of attempting to murder one's officer by usually rolling a fragmentary grenade into his quarters. In Air Force talk, it is short for "fragmentary order".

FACT:

The Tet Offensive was a major turning point of the war. On January 30, 1968, North Vietnamese and Vietcong forces launched attacks intended to capture many provincial capitols, cities, and other targets, including major American bases. While they did overrun much of Hue city and inflict many casualties (including the murdering of hundreds of people), they did not succeed in any objectives. The Vietcong were no longer the force they had been.

American public opinion was shocked by the ability of the enemy to undertake a major offensive when they had supposedly been wiped out already. President Lyndon Johnson later announced he would not seek re-election, and plans to reduce American participation in the war took on new vigor.

42. ___ True or False: "CAP" stood for "Combat Air Patrol" in the Air Force and "Civil Action Project" in the Marines.

43. ___ True or False: The East Asian rating system was the same as the "Bo Derek" one, with "Number one" as the worst or least, and "Number ten" as the best or greatest.

Answer Key

1. E	2. A	3. D	4. B
5. F	6. C	7. B	8. C
9. A	10. B	11. C	12. E
13. B	14. A	15. D	16. B
17. D	18. E	19. A	20. B
21. C	22. C*	23. D**	24. B***
25. A****	26. D	27. E	28. A
29. B	30. C	31. E	32. A
33. B	34. C	35. D	36. D
37. E	38. B	39. A	40. C
41. True	42. True	43. False	

*"Cover your Ass (or Angle)"
**"Date Eligible for Return from Overseas"
***"Keep it Simple, Stupid"
****"Military Assistance Command, Vietnam"

Chapter 5:
WEAPONS

Weapons are the tools of the trade to soldier, sailor, and airman. The Vietnam War saw the use of many old weapons and new ones developed specifically for that conflict.

1. The M-16 rifle was the standard weapon for most combat troops in Vietnam. Which of the following statements are true?

A. The U.S. Air Force adopted the M-16 for its security police before the U.S. Army adopted it
B. The M-16 fired a cartridge of 5.6 mm. rather than the 7.62 NATO cartridge used in the M-14 rifle and M-60 machine gun
C. The M-16 was also available in a shortened carbine version, the CAR-15
D. All of the above

For a while, stories of M-16's jamming (refusing to function) in combat tarnished its reputation. This problem, later solved, was due to:

2. ___ True or False: The mistaken assumption that the M-16 did not need to be cleaned or lubricated like other rifles.

3. ___ True or False: Differences in ammunition. The first M-16's tested used high-grade match ammunition rather than standard service ammunition.

Marine Corps snipers and Army snipers had different methods and used different weapons. Who used which?

4. ___ Army snipers   A. Accurized M-14's with match grade .308
5. ___ USMC snipers   ammunition and scope
                         B. Remington bolt-action hunting rifles
                            ("Varmint Special") in .308 cal., and scope

The Army Special Forces, Navy SEALs and Underwater Demolition Teams, Air Force Combat Controllers, and Aviators used a variety of non-standard firearms and knives. Which firearms were most popular in each group?

6. ___ 12-gauge shotgun (usually Ithaca Model 37)
7. ___ Smith & Wesson .38 caliber revolver (often replaced by commercially purchased .357 Magnum revolvers)
8. ___ Browning Hi-Power 9 mm. automatic pistol
9. ___ Foreign Submachine guns (especially the Swedish K, or British Sten with silencer)

A. Army Special Forces
B. Air Force combat controllers, Security Police, and Combat Security Police
C. Navy SEALs, riverine forces, and Underwater Demolition Teams
D. Aviators

10. ___ True or False: The Vietcong at first relied on captured weapons, those made in "jungle workshops" and surplus weapons supplied by the Communist Chinese, Soviet Union, and Warsaw Pact nations. They finally standardized on the Soviet designed AK-47, the 7.62 mm. automatic Kalashnikov.

The U.S. Army relied on massive use of artillery to decimate enemy concentrations and to fend off massed human wave attacks by Vietcong and North Vietnamese. A large variety of towed and self-propelled artillery pieces saw use. Match each with its official designation:

Towed (two are the same caliber):
11. ___ M101A1
12. ___ M102
13. ___ M114A1

A. 105 mm. howitzer
B. 155 mm. howitzer

Self-propelled
14. ___ M107
15. ___ M108
16. ___ M109
17. ___ M110

A. 105 mm. howitzer
B. 155 mm. howitzer
C. 175 mm. gun
D. 8 inch howitzer

18. The 105 mm. howitzer was the principal artillery piece used by the Army in Vietnam. Its principal advantages were that it was:

A. Easy to manhandle
B. Helicopter portable
C. Capable of a high rate of fire
D. All of the above

The North Vietnamese Army and the Vietcong had their own artillery, too. They used Russian-designed tube artillery, mortars, and bombardment rockets. Rockets were the most portable, and could be fired by remote control or by using timing devices. Which of the following are true?

19. ___ True or False: A Soviet 122 mm. rocket could be carried in 5 man-packs when accompanied by its tube launcher, or in 3 man-packs when propped in firing position with wooden stakes, sandbags, or with a hasty trench or embankment.

20. ___ True or False: Three Chinese Communist 107 mm. rockets could be carried as easily as one 122 mm. rocket. The crew could fire no more than 5 rockets, or 2 salvos, and had to leave within 5 minutes.

21. ___ True or False: These rockets were used mostly against large area targets, rather than very small bases.

22. ___ True or False: By 1969, rockets were the most used V.C. and North Vietnamese artillery weapons in South Vietnam.

23. U.S. artillery was very versatile and mobile. The airborne platform was:

A. An artillery piece mounted on and fired from a CH-47 helicopter
B. A support for a howitzer, helilifted to boggy ground, with the howitzer transported in another helicopter
C. An AH-1G helicopter firing 2.75 inch rockets

The U.S. Army "Claymore" mine was very popular. Which of the following statements are true?

24. ___ True or False: It contained hundreds of steel balls, which fired in a specific direction.

25. ___ True or False: It was marked "FRONT TOWARD ENEMY".

26. ___ True or False: The C-4 explosive was often pilfered to cook rations.

27. Mines and booby traps were a favorite weapon of the Vietcong. They used:

A. Unexploded American shells and dud bombs
B. Captured Claymore mines and hand grenades
C. Chinese Communist grenades with a tripwire, often concealed inside a soft drink can
D. All of the above

28. In urban areas, the bicycle provided a convenient method of terror bombing by the V.C. They would:

A. Send a bicycle rider with a satchel charge on his back plowing into a crowd where he detonated the charge in a suicide attack
B. Pack a bicycle with explosives and a sensitive detonator in a crowded area, to explode when someone moved the bike
C. Use an explosives-crammed bike with a timer fuse, set to go off when the area would be most crowded
D. All of the above
E. B and C only

29. ___ True or False: An American "fire base" consisted of several artillery pieces, supporting infantry troops, and barbed wire and Claymore mine barriers

30. ___ True or False: No American fire base was ever captured or completely overrun by the Vietcong or North Vietnamese.

"Firecracker" and "Beehive" were two anti-personnel rounds used in American artillery pieces. Describe each:

31. ___ Beehive   A. Canister round with flechettes (tiny steel
32. ___ Firecracker   arrows)
                       B. "Improved conventional munitions" plastic,
                          baseball sized bomblets similar to Air Force
                          cluster bomb unit

33. ___ True or False: H and I fire (harassment and interdiction) was renamed I and I fire (intelligence and interdiction).

34. The standard rocket mounted on U.S. Army gunships or aerial rocket artillery helicopters was:

A. 1.75 inches in diameter
B. 2.75 "
C. 3.75 "
D. 4.75 "

35. The STABO rig used by unconventional U.S. forces was:

A. A load-carrying vest that allowed the wearer to carry three times as much ammo as on the regular pistol belt
B. A booby trap made of stretched wire with a hand grenade placed at one end
C. A torso harness rig with ring clips at the shoulders for rapid extraction by helicopter

36. The "airborne platform" was:

A. A square support with adjustable legs on which a howitzer could be placed on boggy ground
B. An Army O-1E Bird Dog light aircraft, used as an artillery spotting plane
C. A helicopter-mounted radar used to detect enemy personnel and equipment
D. A 105 mm. howitzer placed on an HH-53 helicopter and fired against ground targets

According to Vo Nguyen Giap, the ultimate victory over French forces at Dien Bien Phu in May, 1954, was the last gasp of an exhausted, demoralized Viet Minh force which was ready, in case of defeat, to retreat to sanctuaries near the Chinese border.

37. The last French or colonial unit to be overrun, captured, or killed at the battle of Dien Bien Phu, consisted of:

A. General Navarre's personal bodyguards
B. A unit of the French Foreign Legion
C. Moroccan "goumiers"
D. Vietnamese colonial forces

The standard automatic rifles used by both sides in the Vietnam conflict were the Colt M-16 (U.S. and Allies) and the Kalashnikov AK-47 (North Vietnamese and Vietcong). How do they compare?

38. ___ Longer (39" vs. 34.25")   A. M-16
39. ___ Heavier (9.5 lbs. vs. 8.4 lbs.)   B. AK-47
40. ___ Faster rate of fire (700 rounds
    per second vs. 600)
41. ___ Greater muzzle velocity (3,250 feet
    per second vs. 2,350)
42. ___ Green tracers (vs. red)

43. The M-113 armored personnel carrier shown above was the most frequently used armored vehicle during the Vietnam War. It:

A. Was amphibious
B. Had aluminum armor
C. Usually had a bulldozer mounted
D. Was usually seen with troops riding on top
E. All of the above
F. A, B, and D only

44. This bulldozer tank, named "Bad News," is a modification of the American main battle tank most widely used in Vietnam. It is a:

A. M-4 Sherman
B. M-26 Pershing
C. M-48 Patton
D. M-1 Abrams

FACT:

Shown are several types of fighting knives popular among servicemen stationed in Vietnam. They are:

- Marine Corps combat knife, made by Camillus (nearly identical to Ka-Bar WW II combat knife)

- Pilot's survival knife, made by Camillus (Air Force and Navy issue to pilots)

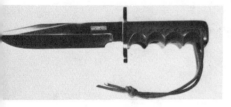

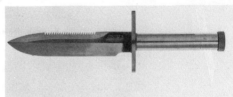

- Randall Model 14, "Attack"

- Randall Model 18

- Gerber Mark I Survival knife (Recondo dagger)

- Gerber Mark II Survival knife

Machine Gun Match: The standard hand-held machine gun used by U.S. and Allied Forces in Vietnam was the M-60 general purpose MG, often nicknamed "the Pig." The M-60 was also mounted on armored vehicles and on helicopters. The .50 cal. Browning M-2 heavy machine gun was used in fixed positions and on armored vehicles. Match each photo to its correct description.

45. ___ M-60 general purpose machine gun, 7.62 mm. Hand-held or mounted on vehicles and helicopters

46. ___ Browning M-2 air-cooled heavy MG, .50 cal. Mounted on armored vehicles, or used in fixed positions

A.

B.

Pick the Pistol: Match each illustration with its correct name.

47. ___ Colt M1911 A-1 .45 auto

48. ___ Browning 9 mm. High Power automatic

49. ___ Smith & Wesson 9mm. Model 39 automatic

A.

B.

C.

Answer Key

1. D	2. True	3. True	4. A
5. B	6. B and C	7. B and D	8. A, B, and C
9. A	10. True	11. A	12. A
13. B	14. C	15. A	16. B
17. D	18. D	19. True	20. True
21. True	22. True	23. B	24. True
25. True	26. True	27. D	28. E
29. True	30. True	31. A	32. B
33. True	34. B	35. C	36. A
37. B	38. A	39. B	40. A
41. A	42. B	43. F	44. C
45. B	46. A	47. C	48. B
49. A			

Chapter 6:
AIR WAR

The air war in Indochina included strategic bombing of North Vietnam, support missions over South Vietnam, and attacks on the Ho Chi Minh Trail in Laos and Cambodia. Enemy sanctuaries in Cambodia were bombed secretly for months before the news was released.

There were two major bombing campaigns over North Vietnam, one from 1965 to 1968, the other in 1972. What were their code names? (Only two answers are correct)

1. ___ 1965 to 1968   A. Linebacker
2. ___ 1972   B.· Tight End
                        C. Spring Rain
                        D. Rolling Thunder

3. U.S. Navy carrier aircraft flew missions against North Vietnam from "Yankee Station", in the Gulf of Tonkin. From 1965 to 1966, one carrier served off South Vietnam at:

A. Dixie Station
B. Zulu Station
C. Gonzo Station
D. Rebel Station

4. The Boeing B-52 Stratofortress, nicknamed BUFF or Big Ugly Flying "Fellow" (a euphemism for another word starting with F), was designed to carry nuclear weapons. The B-52 was modified internally and externally to carry conventional high explosive bombs. What was the maximum bombload?

A. 10,000 lbs. of bombs
B. 14,000 lbs. of bombs
C. 27,000 lbs. of bombs
D. 40,000 lbs. of bombs

5. Before bases in Thailand were capable of handling B-52's, they flew missions from air bases in:

A. The Philippines
B. Malaysia
C. Hawaii
D. Guam

6. The air approaches to North Vietnam were divided up into six "route packages" taken by attacking aircraft. Route Package 6 was:

A. The farthest South, nearest to South Vietnam
B. The farthest North, closest to Communist China
C. The most direct route over Haiphong and Hanoi

Certain targets were "off limits" to U.S. airmen at various times. When did U.S. planes first hit:

7. ___ POL (petroleum, oil and lubricant   A. August 1964
      storage)   B. June 1965
8. ___ MiG fighter bases   C. April 1967
9. ___ PT boat bases

Other early milestones in the air campaigns:

10. ___ First Air Force MiG kills of the war   A. April, 1967
11. ___ First Navy MiG kills   B. July, 1965
12. ___ U.S. Navy air attacks on North Vietnam-   C. June, 1965
       ese oil storage tanks at Haiphong   D. June, 1966
13. ___ First air attacks on MiG airfields defend-
       ing Hanoi area

14. In two bizarre incidents, one in 1967 and one in 1969, American planes badly damaged their own carriers in the Pacific, when:

A. They crashed into the "island" (control tower) causing great loss of life
B. They accidentally launched rockets into the parked aircraft while sitting on deck
C. They fired on the carrier while attempting emergency landings

15. In the air war over Vietnam, Soviet-built Vietnamese Air Force MiG's shot down American aircraft, and vice versa. Navy attack (*not* fighter) aircraft, on three separate occasions, downed MiG-17's. The victors were of two types (choose two answers):

A. A-1 Skyraiders (propeller-driven)
B. A-4 Skyhawk (jet)
C. A-6 Intruder (jet)
D. A-7 Corsair II

16. The F-4 Phantom, used as bomber and fighter by the Air Force, Navy, and Marines, was armed only with missiles, unlike older fighters with 20 mm. cannons. This proved:

A. So successful against enemy aircraft that cannons were replaced with missiles on the other aircraft types
B. Useless in close-range dogfighting. Later, the Phantoms were equipped with 20 mm. Vulcan cannons in a pod or in a completely redesigned nose
C. Neither more or less effective than the cannons in the older aircraft

17. Col. Robin Olds, USAF commander of the 8th Tactical Fighter Wing in 1967, and husband of movie actress Ella Raines:

A. Was a World War II ace with 12 kills in the air and 11 on the ground
B. Became an ace in Vietnam by shooting down 5 MiGs in three flights
C. Was shot down and killed on a mission over North Vietnam
D. All of the above
E. A and B only

18. Black Col. Daniel "Chappie" James was deputy wing commander to Col. Olds. Which of the following was true:

A. The two were sometimes called "Black Man and Robin"
B. James wore a black panther painted on his flight helmet, but this was certainly not in sympathy with the radical "Black Panther" movement in the U.S.
C. Col. James was the son of a former combat pilot, as was Olds
D. All of the above
E. A and B only

Pilot Jargon:

19. ___ Six	A.	Fuel tanks nearly empty
20. ___ Bingo	B.	Warning for anti-radiation
21. ___ Pucker Factor		missile launch
22. ___ Shotgun	C.	The position right behind you
	D.	Graphic description of fear

23. A "Flak Trap" was:

A. The American method for destroying anti-aircraft emplacements
B. A North Vietnamese tactic in which fire was withheld until rescue aircraft approached a downed pilot
C. The belt of anti-aircraft guns around Hanoi, the densest concentration of such weapons in the world
D. The bar back on base, analogous to the golfer's "nineteenth hole"

The Soviet-built-and-supplied SAM anti-aircraft missiles took quite a toll of American warplanes over North Vietnam. Special aircraft equipped with missiles which homed in on radar transmissions fought hard against these installations. Which is which here?

24. ___ Shrike	A.	The code name for the missions against the radar stations and missiles
25. ___ Iron Hand		
26. ___ Wild Weasel	B.	The aircraft carrying the radar-homing missiles
	C.	The radar-homing missiles

27. In the Korean War, American F-86 fighter planes enjoyed a 14-to-1 kill ratio against North Korean MiGs. Up to 1968, the American kill ratio against the North Vietnamese was closer to:

A. 1-to-1
B. 2-to-1
C. 8-to-1
D. 25-to-1

28. This USAF F-4C Phantom II is:

A. Launching rockets against a ground target somewhere in South Vietnam
B. Laying a smokescreen to obscure following aircraft from North Vietnamese radar screens
C. Dumping fuel prior to making an emergency landing at a base in Southeast Asia
D. Dropping marker bombs to pinpoint targets for following aircraft

A.

Navy Aircraft Quiz: Match these USN aircraft names with pictures.

29. ___ Douglas A-1 Skyraider (or Spad or Sandy)
30. ___ Lockheed WV-2 (Air Force designation: EC-121) Constellation
31. ___ LTV F8U or F-8A Crusader

B.

C.

A.

B.

Air Force Attack Aircraft Quiz: Match these, too.

32. ___ LTV A-7 Corsair II (or SLUF)
33. ___ Republic F-105 Thunderchief ("Thud")
34. ___ Northrop F-5 Freedom fighter
35. ___ Cessna A-37 Dragonfly
36. ___ North American F-100 Super Sabre

A.

B.

Forward Air Control Aircraft Identification Quiz: Match each name to the correct photo.

37. ___ Cessna O-1 "Bird Dog"
38. ___ Cessna O-2 "Super Skymaster"
39. ___ North American Rockwell OV-10 "Bronco"

C.

40. The venerable C-47, first flown in civilian form in 1936, was used by the U.S. Air Force and Republic of Vietnam Air Force as:

A. A transport aircraft
B. A psychological warfare aircraft, with loudspeakers and leaflet dropping equipment
C. A heavily armed gunship
D. All of the above

41. ___ True or False: Tail gunners aboard USAF B-52 bombers destroyed 2 MiG fighters during Linebacker II operations over North Vietnam in late 1972.

42. In the Vietnam air war, aerial refueling, in which Air Force or Navy tanker aircraft pumped fuel into other airplanes in flight:

A. Was never used due to the short distances the attack airplanes had to fly
B. Allowed attack planes to take off with higher bomb loads. The fuel tanks were then topped off by tanker aircraft
C. Was sometimes used to keep damaged aircraft returning from raids from running out of fuel which leaked out of perforated fuel tanks
D. B and C above
E. None of the above

Answer Key

1. D	2. A	3. A	4. D
5. D	6. B	7. B	8. C
9. A	10. B	11. C	12. D
13. A	14. B	15. A and B	16. B
17. A	18. E	19. C	20. A
21. D	22. B	23. B	24. C
25. A	26. B	27. B	28. C
29. A	30. B	31. C	32. A
33. C	34. D	35. B	36. E
37. B	38. A	39. C	40. D
41. True	42. D		

Chapter 7:

BLUE WATER AND BROWN WATER

Navy service in Vietnam was divided into the "Blue Water Navy" aboard ships offshore and the "Brown Water Navy" consisting of U.S. and Allied riverine forces.

Brown water riverine force of ATC's (Armored Troop Carriers) provides security as a UH-1 Helicopter lifts off a wounded soldier.

1. The U.S. Coast Guard participated in the Vietnam War:

A. By guarding and supervising port facilities
B. By interdicting enemy shipping both offshore and onshore
C. By providing training to the Vietnamese forces
D. By sending its helicopter pilots to aid USAF search and rescue forces
E. All of the above

2. ___ True or False: U.S. Navy Seabees, known for their remarkable construction projects worldwide in World War II, did not serve in Vietnam.

3. The U.S. Army forces participating in the "Brown Water Navy" included:

A. Barracks vessels carrying infantry who were landed on shore in combat operations
B. Fast RAG ("river assault group") attack boats
C. Artillery barges which were often moored to the shore when firing
D. All of the above
E. A and B only
F. A and C only

U.S. and Allied naval forces patrolled Vietnamese waters to control enemy infiltration of men, weapons and supplies from North Vietnam to South Vietnam. What were the code names for these operations?

4. ___ Offshore counterinfiltration
5. ___ Onshore and riverine operations

A. Endsweep
B. Game Warden
C. Ranch Hand
D. Market Time

6. The Gulf of Tonkin incident in August of 1964 prompted major American attacks against North Vietnam. In this incident, two American destroyers were attacked by North Vietnamese:

A. MiG-15 aircraft
B. Submarines
C. Torpedo Boats
D. Cruisers

7. On July 19, 1972, the picket destroyer USS *Biddle* (DLG-34) was attacked by 5 North Vietnamese Air Force MiGs. The outcome of this attack was:

A. The severe damage of the *Biddle,* forcing its withdrawal to Subic Bay Naval Base for major repairs
B. The sinking of the *Biddle,* the only major U.S. naval vessel sunk by the North Vietnamese
C. The destruction of two MiGs, one by gunfire and one by anti-aircraft missiles launched by the *Biddle*
D. Inconclusive, as neither the MiGs nor the *Biddle* damaged each other

8. The Grumman F-14 Tomcat, the Navy's current interceptor, was used during the Vietnamese conflict, flying from the USS *Enterprise* on which occasion(s):

A. Combat air patrols during Linebacker II mission over North Vietnam in December, 1972
B. Flying cover during the week after the January, 1973 cease-fire
C. Flying top cover during the final 1975 American evacuation of South Vietnam as the Communists overran Saigon

FACT:

On November 22, 1970, U.S. Navy SEAL teams in a secret operation freed American POW's from a Vietcong prison camp within South Vietnam. This operation is still virtually unknown by most Americans.

9. The last action taken by the U.S. Navy in Vietnam was Operation Endsweep, the clearing of the port of Haiphong of American-sown mines. The minesweeping was performed by:

A. U.S. Navy and Coast Guard minesweepers which were taken out of mothballs expressly for the action
B. Large HH-53 helicopters towing sleds with mine detection equipment
C. Drone helicopters towing mine detection sleds
D. Navy UDT divers using old-fashioned diving suits

FACTS:

The battleship USS *New Jersey* (BB-62) was recommissioned in 1968 to provide fire support off Vietnam, served there briefly, and was decommissioned in 1969. She had a crew of 70 officers and 1556 enlisted men and served a 120-day tour off Vietnam with 47 days at sea at one time. In 1983, The USS *New Jersey* supported the Multilateral Force in Lebanon.

A.

B.

C.

The vessels shown here are (match name with photo):

10. ___ Typical Vietnamese junk
11. ___ PBR (River patrol boat)
12. ___ PCE (Inshore patrol craft)

13. ___ True or False: The *New Jersey* fired more rounds in the Vietnam War than in either World War II or Korea.

14. This Navy enlisted man is:

A. Arming a 16″ shell aboard USS *New Jersey*
B. Fusing a 500-lb. bomb under the wing of an attack plane aboard USS *America* (CVA-66)
C. Placing a plug in the underwing fuel tank of a fighter plane aboard USS *Ticonderoga*

15. Two attack aircraft from the carrier USS *Constellation* head for targets in North Vietnam. They are:

A. A-1 Skyraiders
B. A-4 Skyhawks
C. A-6 Intruders

16. Shown here are the two U.S. Navy destroyers involved in the Tonkin Gulf Incident used as a rationale for American attacks against North Vietnam in 1964. What are their names?

A. USS *Forrest Sherman*
B. USS *Maddox*
C. USS *The Sullivans*
D. USS *Turner Joy*

Answer Key

1. E	2. False	3. F	4. D
5. B	6. C	7. C*	8. C
9. B	10. A	11. C	12. B
13. True	14. B	15. C	16. D (p. 64)
			B (p. 65)

*The <u>Biddle</u> was unharmed.

Chapter 8:

CHOPPER I.D.

The helicopter used as a weapon and for transport came into its own during The Vietnam War. Adaptable for use everywhere in Indochina, the chopper was a common sight to U.S. Forces of all services as well as the American television audience following the war on the evening news.
See if you can identify these choppers and correctly match them to their names.

1. ___ Kaman HH-43 Husky

2. ___ Bell HU-1B Iroquois ("Huey")

3. ___ Bell OH-58 Kiowa

4. ___ Bell AH-1 Cobra

5. ___ Hughes OH-6 Cayuse ("Loach")

6. ___ Sikorsky HH-3E ("Jolly Green Giant")

7. ___ Sikorsky HH-53E ("Big Mother")

A.

B.

C.

D.

E.

F.

G.

A HU-1D Medevac chopper (Dustoff Ship) with Red Cross on door evacuates casualty from a typical American fire base in South Vietnam.

8. ____ True or False: The Vietcong and North Vietnamese scrupulously obeyed the Geneva Convention and never deliberately fired on medical helicopters bearing a red cross.

Answer Key

1. D   2. A   3. E   4. F
5. B   6. G   7. C   8. False

Chapter 9:
SPECIAL FORCES

The U.S. Army Special Forces, formed at Fort Bragg in the late 1950's and known as the Green Berets, were widely publicized in the earlier days of the Vietnam War. The Army, Navy, and Marine Corps had other special elite forces, too.

Which of these forces was which?

1. ___ CIDG	A.	Small U.S. Army patrols who operated in enemy-controlled areas to gather intelligence
2. ___ Ruff-Puff		
3. ___ LRRP	B.	Local ethnic Vietnamese defense forces
4. ___ MACV-SOG	C.	Regular South Vietnamese Army
5. ___ ARVN	D.	Non-Vietnamese ethnic groups supported by U.S. Special Forces
	E.	Secret U.S. Forces who performed many mysterious duties

6. The major purpose of Army Special Forces was:

A. Counterintelligence, i.e., finding Vietcong sympathizers among forces "loyal" to the U.S.
B. Training and assisting non-Vietnamese forces, particularly Montagnards in the Central Highlands
C. Assassination of Vietcong officials
D. Providing security for artillery fire bases

7. The basic unit of the Special Forces was the "A-Team" which consisted of:

A. 19-20 men under a Lt. Col.
B. 24 men under a Major
C. 12 men under a Captain

8. The basic A-Team contained a number of specialists, all of whom were cross-trained in at least one other specialty. These specialties included:

A. Heavy Weapons
B. Medical specialties
C. Intelligence
D. Military Engineering
E. All of the above
F. All but D above

FACT:
Camouflage uniforms, now standard issue to all U.S. Army troops, were used in Vietnam most often by special operations forces. Among the popular types were:

- French "lizard" pattern, used by Vietnamese paratroopers
- Spotted "duck hunter" pattern, similar to USMC WW II issue
- "Tiger Stripe" pattern, developed in Vietnam, used by Vietnamese, American, and Australian forces primarily
- The four-color "leaf" pattern, also used on helmet covers

9. Army LRRP companies were under the supervision of:

A. The Special Forces
B. The 75th Infantry (Army Rangers)
C. U.S. Army Commando Teams
D. The 11th Armored Division

10. The job of the "Phoenix" committees (in Vietnamese, Phung Huaong) was:

A. Assassinating V.C. officials, euphemistically called, "eliminating the V.C. infrastructure"
B. Organizing village chiefs and trying to win them over to the South Vietnamese government side
C. Investigating Vietnamese Army units to uncover corruption and morale problems
D. Raising forces among former Vietcong who had rallied to the Allied cause

The Mobile Strike ("Mike") Forces, and Project Delta were two attempts to hit at the Vietcong and North Vietnamese, especially by monitoring and controlling infiltration from the North. Who was who?

11. ___ Mike Forces   A.   Nungs (ethnic Chinese) forces under U.S.
12. ___ Project Delta   Special Forces; formed in 1964 and mainly used to block Ho Chi Minh Trail traffic
                           B.   Recon and "Roadrunner" teams who monitored Ho Chi Minh Trail traffic and often lured NVA or V.C. into attacks

13. "Roadrunners" operating on the Ho Chi Minh Trail:

A. Disguised themselves as North Vietnamese soldiers or Vietcong
B. Used enemy equipment and weapons
C. Accompanied enemy units, reported on their location, and often led them into ambushes or air strikes
D. All of the above

14. Special Forces units officially left South Vietnam:

A. In 1969
B. In 1971
C. In 1973
D. In 1975

15. The "MacNamara Wall" was an attempt to control enemy infiltration. How many of the following statements are true:

A. It was intended to consist of a system of sensors, physical barriers, and troop units to control enemy movement
B. It would have extended across the DMZ (Demilitarized Zone) between North and South Vietnam, and into Laos
C. Construction was halted in early 1968 and the "Wall" was never completed
D. All of the above
E. A and C only

16. Lima Sites were:

A. Special Forces bases in the Central Highlands
B. Landing strips and base areas in Laos
C. Navy SEAL bases concealed in the Mekong Delta
D. Designated targets on the Ho Chi Minh Trail

17. In November, 1970, nearly 100 American assault troops with air support landed at a North Vietnamese prison camp at Son Tay in an attempt to rescue the American prisoners. What were the results of the raid?

A. The assault force originally landed at a nearby NVA base in error, but shot it up before heading to the prison camp
B. The assault force rescued only a few prisoners before forced to withdraw by heavy North Vietnamese fire
C. The raid found no prisoners, since they had been removed earlier, but the force killed many North Vietnamese and their Communist bloc advisors
D. A and B only
E. A and C only

18. After the Son Tay raid:

A. The North Vietnamese treated its prisoners a bit better, and centralized them in fewer, bigger, camps
B. The North Vietnamese were proven vulnerable to invasion
C. The North Vietnamese treated their prisoners much worse, and dispersed them to small camps in the countryside
D. A and B only
E. B and C only

Answer Key

1. D*	2. B**	3. A***	4. E****
5. C	6. B	7. C	8. E
9. B	10. A	11. A	12. B
13. D	14. B	15. D	16. A
17. E	18. D		

*Civilian Irregular Defense Groups
**Regional Forces/Popular Forces
***Long Range Reconnaisance Patrols
****Military Assistance Command Vietnam,
Studies and Operations Group

Chapter 10:
BODY COUNT:
STATISTICS AND DATES

"Body counts", or counts of the enemy dead after operations, were supposed to show how the Vietcong and North Vietnamese were being decimated during the war. These counts could be very inaccurate, since the enemy often carried off their dead and wounded. Many body counts were estimated or inflated as they were passed up channels to higher headquarters.

The United States Air Force lost many aircraft in combat and operations in Southeast Asia during the Vietnam Conflict, and many aircrews were captured or taken prisoner. On the encouraging side, the Aerospace Rescue and Recovery Service of the USAF managed to save many lives, often at great risk to the rescuers, who were shot at by the Vietcong and North Vietnamese.

1. ___ Number of aircraft lost   A. 885
2. ___ Aircrews killed, captured or missing   B. 1,763
3. ___ Lives saved by ARRS (AF rescue   C. 2,254
     crews)   D. 3,883

The French Armies and their Indochinese National Armies lost many men in their conflict from 1946 to 1954.

4. ___ French killed or MIA   A. 31,716
5. ___ French wounded   B. 65,125
6. ___ Casualties, Indochinese Allies   C. 75,867

7. Three percent of hospitalized soldiers in World War II had suffered eye injuries. The percentage in Vietnam was:

A. Less than one percent
B. About three percent, the same as World War II
C. Nine percent
D. Thirty-eight percent

After the 1954 Geneva Agreement in which Vietnam was divided into North and South, large numbers of people moved from North to South or vice versa. Communist sympathizers and others moved north. Those who moved south were mostly Catholics from the area Southeast of the Red River delta. What were the numbers involved?

8. ___ Up to 90,000   A. South to North
9. ___ 90,000 to 150,000   B. North to South

In order to qualify for veteran's benefits, a serviceman or woman had to serve active duty between what dates? (Periods of active duty for Reserve or National Guard training do not count)

10. ___ Starting date   A. January 1, 1961
                                 B. August 5, 1964
                                 C. June 5, 1967

11. ___ Closing date   A. May 5, 1970
                                 B. January 25, 1973
                                 C. May 7, 1975

The number of U.S. troops increased vastly as we took over more and more of the burden of the war. As Vietnamization began, these numbers dwindled. What were approximate American troop strengths in Vietnam as of the following dates? (Note: Use one answer twice)

12. ___ Late 1965   A. 180,000
13. ___ Mid-1969   B. 550,000
14. ___ Mid-1971   C. 27,000
15. ___ Late 1972

16. The President of the United States once said:

"The United States would supply aid for maintaining a strong, viable state, capable of resisting attempted subversion or aggression through military means . . . The United States expects this aid will be met by performance on the part of the Government of Vietnam in undertaking needed reforms."

Who said this and when?

A. Dwight D. Eisenhower in October, 1954
B. Lyndon B. Johnson in January, 1969
C. Richard M. Nixon in July, 1974

17. Richard M. Nixon had a plan to end the war. It included withdrawal of U.S. forces, and turning the war over to the Vietnamese ("Vietnamization"). On what date did he announce the withdrawal of the first 25,000 American troops?

A. November 10, 1968
B. January 1, 1969
C. June 8, 1969
D. May 8, 1970

18. The cease-fire which ended direct American involvement in Vietnam, took effect on:

A. May 8, 1970
B. January 25, 1972
C. January 25, 1973
D. May 25, 1975

19. The siege of Dien Bien Phu in 1954 and the final North Vietnamese campaign which defeated South Vietnam in 1975 both lasted the same number of days:

A. 23
B. 55
C. 118
D. 225

20. The Viet Minh used strengthened and modified Peugeot bicycles as transports during their successful war against the French. In the war against the United States and South Vietnam, the North Vietnamese again used bicycles to ferry supplies down the Ho Chi Minh Trail. This time the bicycles were mostly of Chinese make and could carry:

A. 50 kilograms (110 lbs.)
B. 100 kg (220 lbs.)
C. 225 kg (almost 500 lbs.)

21. Two of the three American commanders in Vietnam had very similar careers. Both were former CO's of the 101st Airborne and commandants of West Point, and both went on to become chairmen of the Joint Chiefs of Staff. Which of the three was none of these, but was an armored division commander under George Patton in World War II?

A. Maxwell Taylor
B. William Westmoreland
C. Creighton Abrams

22. Daniel Ellsberg, who leaked the Pentagon Papers to the New York *Times,* had previously been:

A. A U.S. Marine artillery officer in Vietnam
B. A U.S. Information Agency representative in Thailand
C. A U.S. State Department official in Vietnam
D. A war correspondent for the Chicago *Tribune*

23. The peak number of U.S. troops serving in Vietnam was over half a million. This number was reached in:

A. March, 1967
B. July, 1968
C. April, 1969
D. January, 1970

24. Kit Carson scouts were:

A. Specially recruited from game wardens, forest rangers, and park rangers in rural areas of the U.S.
B. Former Vietcong who had "rallied" to the Allied cause
C. American Indians who served as trackers on long-range patrols

The air war over Indochina continued from the early 1960's until the end of American participation. How did each of the following airmen reach distinction:

25. Capt. Lance P. Sijan
26. Capt. Charles DeBellevue
27. Major Bernard Fisher
28. Lt. Everett Alvarez

A. First pilot captured by the North Vietnamese
B. First Air Force pilot to receive Medal of Honor in Vietnam
C. Leading American ace of the war
D. First Air Force Academy graduate to be awarded the Medal of Honor

THE "WALL"

FACTS:

- The Vietnam Veterans Memorial was dedicated on Veterans' Day, 1982.

- Contains the names of the dead and missing in letters about ½ inch high and .015 inch deep engraved on 150 panels of black Vermont granite. A memorial statue depicting three combat infantry in jungle fatigues faces the "wall".

- Was designed by Maya Lin, an Asian-American woman at Yale University.

29. ___ True or False: The names of the dead and missing are listed alphabetically.

30. ___ True or False: There are about 58,000 names on the memorial.

31. ___ True or False: The sculptor of the Vietnam War Memorial statue, 38-year-old Frederick Hart, of Washington, D.C., never served in Vietnam. During an anti-war demonstration, he was tear-gassed.

Answer Key

1. C	2. B	3. D	4. C
5. B	6. A	7. C	8. A
9. B	10. B*	11. C*	12. A
13. B	14. A	15. C	16. A
17. C	18. C	19. B	20. C
21. C	22. C	23. C	24. B
25. D	26. C	27. B	28. A
29. False	30. True	31. True	

*Those who served between these dates are considered "Vietnam Era Veterans".

ACTIVE ARMY DIVISIONS IN THE VIETNAM WAR

1st Infantry Division
"The Big Red One"
Organized June 8, 1917

4th Infantry Division
"Ivy Division"
Organized December 10, 1917

5th Infantry Division (Mechanized)
"Red Diamond"
Organized December 11, 1917

9th Infantry Division
No Designation
Organized July 18, 1918

25th Infantry Division
"Tropic Lightning"
Activated October 1, 1941

1st Cavalry Division (Airmobile)
"The First Team"
Activated September 13, 1921

101st Airborne Division (Airmobile)
"Screaming Eagles"
Organized November 2, 1918

23rd Infantry Division
"Americal"
Activated as Americal Division
May 27, 1942

82nd Airborne Division
"All American"
Organized August 25, 1917

FURTHER READING

The number of books published about the Vietnam War increased enormously in the early 1980's. The process continues today. The U.S. Army, Navy, Air Force, and Marine Corps official histories and special studies are in progress. A number of volumes are available, and the series should be completed in the early 1990's. Write to the Superintendent of Documents, Washington, D.C., 20401, and request Subject Bibliography No. 98, Military History, or write to "Books", P.O. Box 37000, Washington D.C., 20013, for the GPO's illustrated catalog, including many Vietnam books.

Squadron/Signal Publishers have many "In Action Books" richly illustrated with photos and drawings of aircraft, ships, armored vehicles, and weapons used in Vietnam. Squadron/Signal has published Lou Drendel's 3-volume set, *Air War Over Southeast Asia* (Carrollton, Texas: Squadron/Signal, 1982-84). A thorough, illustrated account of tanks and armored vehicles in Vietnam appears in Simon Dunstan's *Vietnam Tracks: Armor in Battle, 1945-1975* (Novato, California: Presidio Press, 1983). Stackpole Books, of Harrisburg, Pennsylvania is U.S. distributor for the British publisher Osprey, whose "Men-At-Arms" and "Elite" series portray the often colorful uniforms and equipment used in Vietnam.

Personal accounts of Vietnam service abound. The best of the air war is Col. Jack Broughton's classic *Thud Ridge* (Philadelphia and New York: Lippincott, 1969). Col. Broughton carried a tape recorder in the cockpit on missions over the north, and the dialogue in his book is dramatic and real. An anthology of impressions of service by many authors appears in *Touring Nam: The Vietnam War Reader,* edited by Martin Greenberg and Augustus Norton (New York: Morrow, 1985). Charles R. Anderson's two books: *The Grunts* (Berkeley, California: Berkeley Publishing, 1984) and *Vietnam: The Other War* (Novato, California: Presidio Press, 1982), are accounts of combat service and administrative duties.

Two excellent combat novels are John Del Vecchio's *The 13th Valley* (New York: Bantam, 1982), a paperback about the war in northern South Vietnam, and Kenn Miller's *Tiger the Lurp Dog* (Boston: Little, Brown, 1983) which takes the reader on long-range patrols in enemy areas.

The Vietnam Bookstore, Box 122, Collinsville, Connecticut 06022 offers through the mail a free catalog with a wide selection of fiction and nonfiction books and official U.S. government publications about the Vietnam War, as well as the *Vietnam Newsletter,* an informative journal.

ORDER NOW...
WORLD WAR II TRIVIA QUIZ BOOK, VOLUME 2, THE PACIFIC

"**Erhard Konerding's TRIVIA QUIZ BOOK, VOLUME 2: THE PACIFIC is as:**

Felicitous as MacArthur's Hollandia strategy

Unbeatable as the second wave at Tarawa

Necessary as Atabrine to understanding the Pacific War."

— *William Manchester*

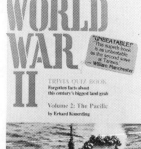

To reserve a copy of WORLD WAR II TRIVIA QUIZ BOOK Volume 2 **return the form below, along with your check in the correct amount, to:**

Southfarm Press, P.O. Box 1296, Middletown, CT 06457

_____ Number of copies WORLD WAR II TRIVIA QUIZ BOOK Volume 2: The Pacific

Name _____

Address _____

City _____ State _____ ZIP _____

Payment enclosed: $_____ .

Note: Price per book is $ 6.95 (U.S. dollars) PLUS $1.00 postage and handling

MONEY-BACK GUARANTEE.
Please allow 4 to 6 weeks for delivery.